# The Little Chicks Sing

*A Traditional Song from Latin America*

retold by Miryam Acevedo-Bouchard
and Kathryn Corbett
illustrated by Gerardo Suzán Prone

**HARCOURT BRACE & COMPANY**

Orlando  Atlanta  Austin  Boston  San Francisco  Chicago  Dallas  New York
Toronto  London

"Peep, peep, pío!"
the little chicks sing.

"We need food! We are cold!
Take us under your wing!"

Mother Hen says,
"Here is corn you can eat.

Then come under my wings and sit by my feet."

Under her wings
the little chicks sleep

until the next day—then

"Pío, peep, peep!"